Gold Stars®

Starting to Write

horse

hen

hay

PaRragon

Bath · New York · Cologne · Melbourne · Delhi
Hong Kong · Shenzhen · Singapore · Amsterdam

Helping your child

⭐ Remember that the activities in this book should be enjoyed by your child. Try to find a quiet place to work.

⭐ Your child does not need to complete each page in one go. Always stop before your child grows tired, and come back to the same page another time.

⭐ It is important to work through the pages in the right order because the activities do get progressively more difficult.

⭐ The answers to the activities are on page 32.

⭐ Always give your child lots of encouragement and praise.

⭐ Remember that the gold stars are a reward for effort as well as for achievement.

This edition published by Parragon Books Ltd in 2015

Parragon Books Ltd
Chartist House
15–17 Trim Street
Bath BA1 1HA, UK
www.parragon.com

Illustrated by Simon Abbott
Written by Betty Root
Educational consultant: Stephanie Cooper

ISBN 978-1-4723-5687-1

Printed in China

Contents

Making patterns   4

Go together   6

Draw the balls   7

Shadows   8

Straight and curvy lines 10

What shall I eat?   12

Curly tails   13

Safari park   14

Flying kites   15

Big and little circles   16

Motor mazes   17

Under the sea   18

Writing letters 1   19

Writing letters 2   20

Writing letters 3   22

Writing letters 4   24

Writing letters 5   26

Capital letters   28

Writing names   30

Writing labels   31

Answers   32

Making patterns

Trace over the dotted lines. Make a row underneath.

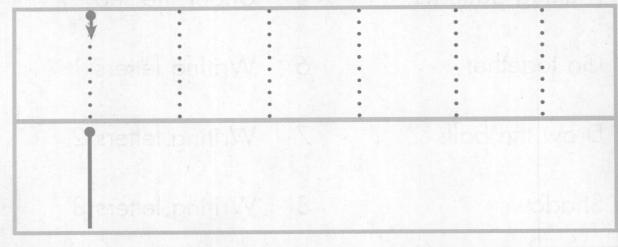

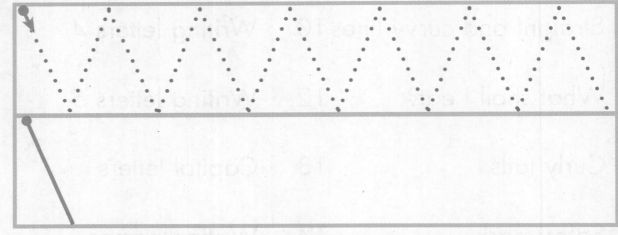

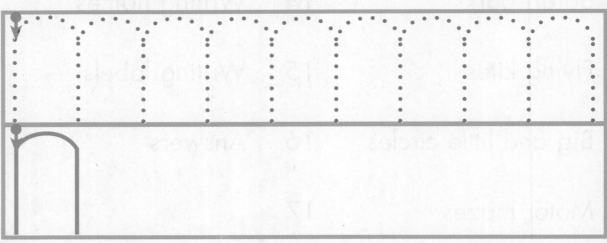

Note for parent: This activity gives practice in pencil control in preparation for letter shapes.

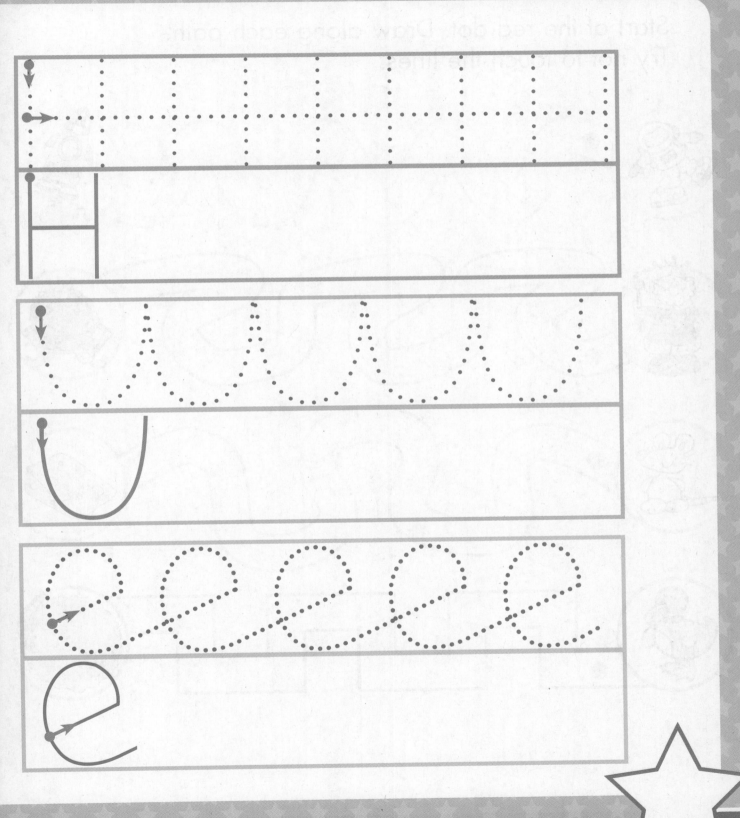

Go together

Start at the red dot. Draw along each path.
Try not to touch the lines.

Note for parent: Keeping between the lines helps pencil control.

Draw the balls

Draw the 5 footballs for the goalie to catch,
then colour the picture.
Draw the little circles around your picture too.

Note for parent: Drawing like this is a good way to develop pre-writing skills.

7

Shadows

Draw lines to join each picture to its shadow.
Try to make straight lines.
The first one has been done for you.

Note for parent: This activity gives children practice in pencil control for straight and wiggly lines.

Draw lines to join each picture to its shadow.
Try to make wiggly lines.
The first one has been done for you.

Straight and curvy lines

Draw over the dotted lines to finish the picture.

Note for parent: This activity helps children to use a pencil carefully to complete pictures.

Colour the picture.

What shall I eat?

Start at the red dot. Draw along each path to find out what everyone eats.

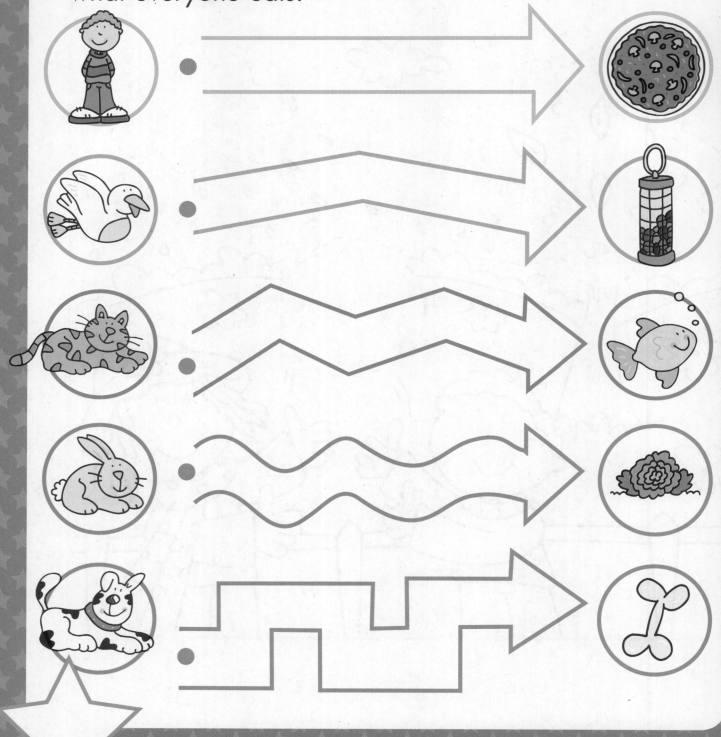

Note for parent: Drawing between two lines encourages pencil control.

Curly tails

Join the dots to draw the tails on the animals, then colour them in.

Note for parent: Children need to develop a steady hand for good writing.

13

Safari park

Draw circles and curvy lines to finish this picture, then colour it in.

Note for parent: This activity helps children to use a pencil carefully to complete pictures.

Flying kites

Draw over the dotted lines, then colour the kites to match the T-shirts.

Note for parent: This gives children practice in controlling the direction of their pencil.

15

Big and little circles

Trace the circles, then the patterns inside them.

Note for parent: This activity gives children further practice in pencil control.

Motor mazes

Trace over the dotted lines to find out which car gets to the finish first.

Note for parent: This gives children practice in controlling the direction of their pencil.

17

Under the sea

Trace the fish and their patterns then colour them in.

Note for parent: This activity helps children to follow dotted lines to make a pattern.

Trace over each dotted letter.

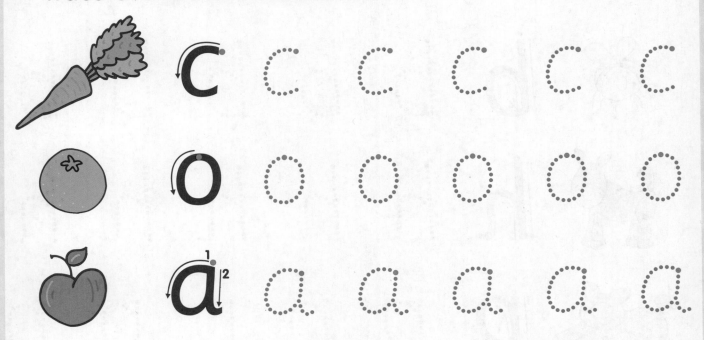

c c c c c c

o o o o o o

a a a a a a

Trace the letters to finish these words.

orange

apple

carrot

Note for parent: These letters start in the same way, so it's helpful to see them together.

Trace over each dotted letter.

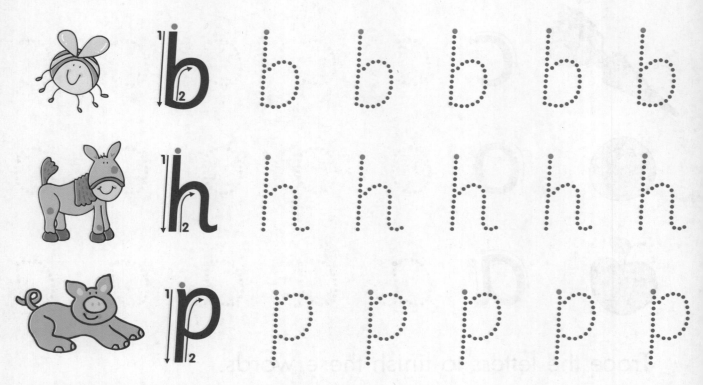

Trace the letters to finish these words.

Note for parent: These letters start in the same way, so it's helpful to see them together.

Trace over each dotted letter.

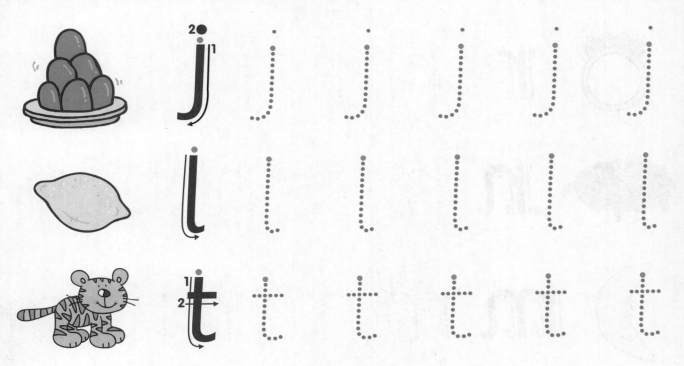

j j j j j j

l l l l l l

t t t t t t

Trace the letters to finish these words.

jelly

lemon

tiger

Trace over each dotted letter.

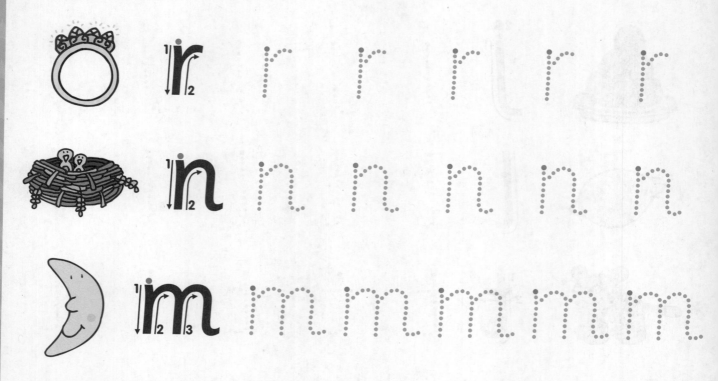

Trace the letters to finish these words.

ring

nest

moon

Trace over each dotted letter.

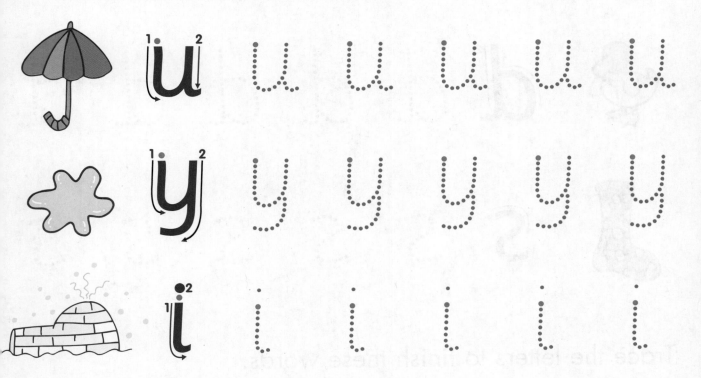

Trace the letters to finish these words.

umbrella

yellow

igloo

Trace over the dotted letters.

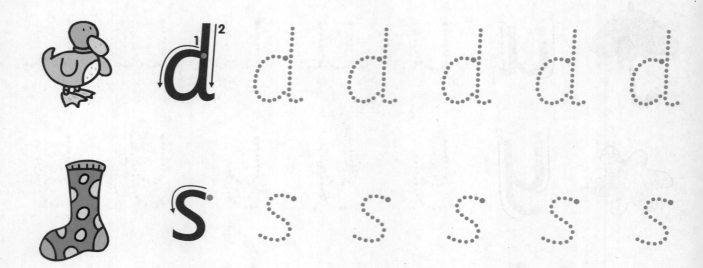

d d d d d d

s s s s s s

Trace the letters to finish these words.

duck

sock

Note for parent: These letters start in the same way, so it's helpful to see them together.

Trace over the dotted letters.

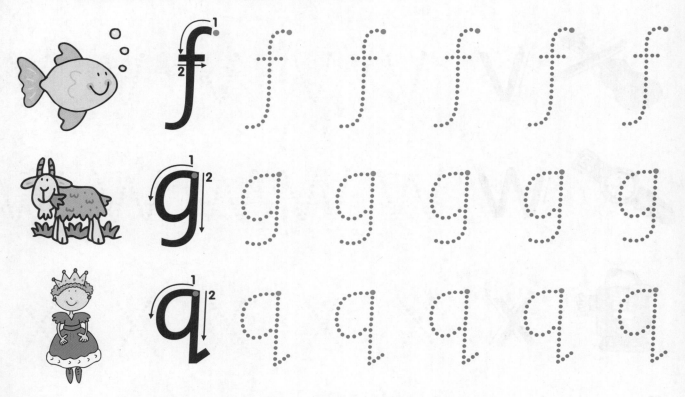

Trace the letters to finish these words.

fish

goat

queen

Trace over the dotted letters.

Trace the letters to finish these words.

violin

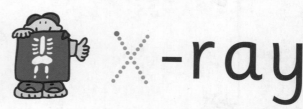
x-ray

watch

Note for parent: These letters start in the same way, so it's helpful to see them together.

Trace over the dotted letters.

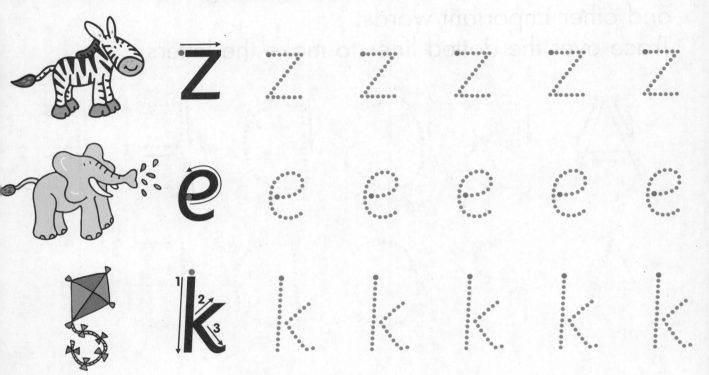

z z z z z z

e e e e e e

k k k k k k

Trace the letters to finish these words.

zebra

elephant

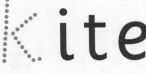

kite

Capital letters are used at the beginning of names and other important words.
Trace over the dotted lines to make the letters.

Note for parent: This activity helps children to learn to write all the capital letters.

N O P Q R S T

N O P Q R S T

U V W X Y Z

U V W X Y Z

Writing names

All names begin with a capital letter.
Write the names and colour the pictures.

Mummy

Daddy

Draw a picture of yourself and write your name.

Draw a picture of someone else you know and write their name.

Note for parent: This activity helps children to learn that names begin with a capital letter.

Trace over the dotted letters to label each toy.

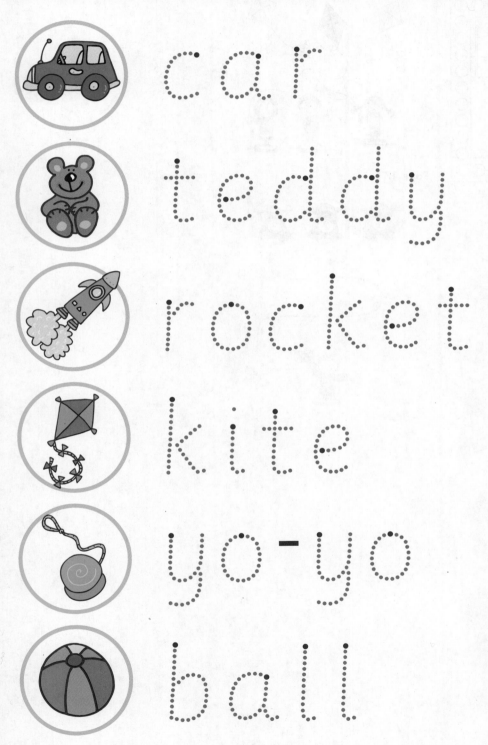

car

teddy

rocket

kite

yo-yo

ball

Note for parent: This activity gives practice in writing and matching letters.

31

Answers

Page 7

Pages 8–9

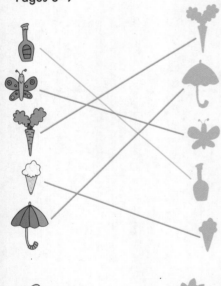

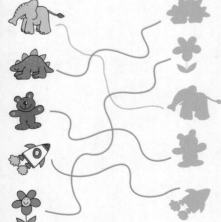

Page 15

Page 17